Ladybird  Readers

The Tale of Peter Rabbit

Series Editor: Sorrel Pitts

Text adapted by Sorrel Pitts

LADYBIRD BOOKS

UK | USA | Canada | Ireland | Australia
India | New Zealand | South Africa

Ladybird Books is part of the Penguin Random House group of companies
whose addresses can be found at global.penguinrandomhouse.com.
www.penguin.co.uk   www.puffin.co.uk   www.ladybird.co.uk

Based on the original tale by Beatrix Potter
This 'Ladybird Readers' edition first published 2018
001

Printed in China

A CIP catalogue record for this book is available from the British Library

ISBN: 978-0-241-31614-6

All correspondence to
Ladybird Books
Penguin Random House Children's
80 Strand, London WC2R 0RL

MIX
Paper from
responsible sources
FSC® C018179

Ladybird Readers

The Tale of Peter Rabbit

Based on the original tale
by Beatrix Potter

Picture words

mother

Peter Rabbit

sisters

farmer

garden

shed

berries

radish

This is Peter Rabbit.

Peter is with his mother
and his three sisters.

"Don't go in the
farmer's garden,"
says Peter's mother.

Peter's sisters want
some berries for
dinner. They go in
their mother's garden.

Peter Rabbit wants some radishes. He goes in the farmer's garden.

Peter eats lots
of radishes.

Oh no! The farmer sees
Peter Rabbit.

"Oh no!" says
Peter Rabbit.

He runs from the farmer.

The farmer runs after
Peter. The farmer cannot
catch him.

Peter Rabbit
runs in the shed.
The farmer goes
in the shed, too.

The farmer
sees Peter!

Peter Rabbit runs
from the shed.

The farmer runs after
Peter again. He cannot
catch him.

Peter Rabbit runs from the farmer's garden.

Peter runs and runs!

23

Peter Rabbit goes home.

"Go to bed!" Peter's mother says. "No dinner for you!"

Peter Rabbit goes to bed.

Peter Rabbit's sisters
eat the berries
for dinner.

Activities

The key below describes the skills practiced in each activity.

🖊 Spelling and writing

📖 Reading

💬 Speaking

❓ Critical thinking

✳ Preparation for the Cambridge Young Learners exams

1 Circle the correct pictures.

1 This is Peter Rabbit.

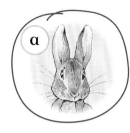 a
 b
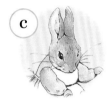 c

2 This is Peter's mother.

 a
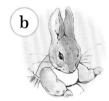 b
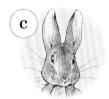 c

3 These are Peter's sisters.

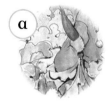 a
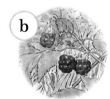 b
 c

4 This is the farmer.

 a
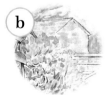 b
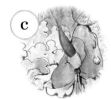 c

2 **Look and read. Write *yes* or *no*.**

This is Peter Rabbit.

Peter is with his mother and his three sisters.

6   7

1 Peter Rabbit is with his
mother.   ....yes.......

2 Peter Rabbit is with his
four sisters.   ....

3 Peter Rabbit's mother
has four children.   ....

4 Peter Rabbit has a
mother and three sisters.   ....

5 Peter Rabbit has
three brothers.   ....

3 **Look and read. Put a** **or a** **in the boxes.**

"Don't go in the farmer's garden," says Peter's mother.

Peter's sisters want some berries for dinner. They go in their mother's garden.

8

1 "Go in the farmer's garden," says Peter's mother. ✗

2 "Don't go in the farmer's garden," says Peter's mother. ✓

3 Peter's sisters go in their mother's garden.

4 Peter's sisters want some radishes for dinner.

5 Peter's sisters want some berries for dinner.

4 **Circle the correct sentences.**

1
  a This is a garden.
  b This is a farmer.

2
  a These are sisters.
  b These are berries.

3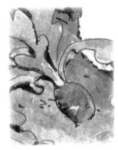
  a This is a radish.
  b This is a rabbit.

4
  a This is a mother.
  b This is a shed.

5 Look and read. Choose the correct words, and write them on the lines.

"Don't go in the farmer's garden," says Peter's mother.

Peter's sisters want some berries for dinner. They go in their mother's garden.

Peter Rabbit wants some radishes. He goes in the farmer's garden.

---

sisters   lots of   radishes   berries

---

1 Peter Rabbit's .... sisters .... like berries.

2 Peter wants some ....

3 Peter's mother has .... in her garden.

4 The farmer has .... radishes.

6 **Ask and answer the questions with a friend.** 🗨 ❓

Peter eats lots of radishes.

1 Where is Peter?

He is in the farmer's garden.

2 What does Peter eat?

3 Does he eat one radish?

4 Does Peter like radishes?

7 Do the crossword.

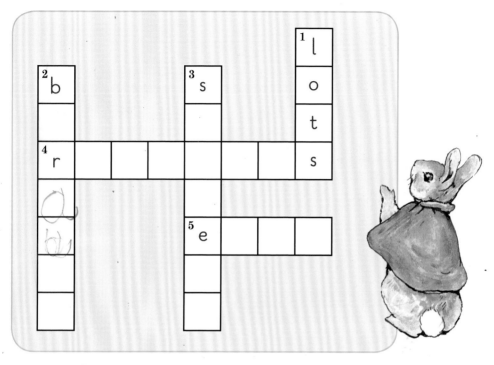

Across

4 Peter wants some of these.

5 Peter . . . radishes in the farmer's garden.

Down

1 Peter eats . . . of radishes

2 Peter's sisters want these for dinner.

3 Peter has three . . .

8 **Read the questions.**
Write the answers. 📖 ✏️

1 Does Peter have three sisters?

Yes, he has three sisters.

2 Does Peter's mother have a garden?

3 Does the farmer have a garden?

4 Does Peter eat the farmer's berries?

9 **Complete the sentences.**
Write a—d.

1 Oh no! The farmer sees .... C ....

2 Peter runs from ....

3 The farmer runs ....

4 The farmer cannot ....

a the farmer.

b catch him.

c Peter Rabbit.

d after Peter.

10 Circle the correct words.

Peter Rabbit
runs in the shed.
The farmer goes
in the shed, too.

The farmer
sees Peter!

18

19

1 Peter Rabbit **walks. / runs.**

2 Peter Rabbit runs in the
house. / shed.

3 The **farmer / friend**
goes in the shed, too.

4 The farmer sees
Peter's mother! / Peter!

11 **Read the text. Choose the correct words and write them next to 1—4.** 📖 ✏️ ✳️

Peter Rabbit runs from the shed.

The farmer runs after Peter again. He cannot catch him.

Peter Rabbit runs from the farmer's garden.

Peter runs and runs!

from   after   garden   catch

Peter Rabbit runs [1] _from_

the shed. The farmer runs

[2] _____ Peter again.

He cannot [3] _____ Peter.

Peter runs from the farmer's

[4] _____.

12 **Look and read. Write *Go*, *go*, or *goes*.**

Peter Rabbit goes home.

"Go to bed!" Peter's mother says. "No dinner for you!"

Peter Rabbit goes to bed.

24 25

1 Peter Rabbit ......goes...... home.

2 " .... to bed!" Peter's mother says.

3 Peter .... to bed.

4 Peter's sisters do not .... to bed.

13 **Talk to your friend about Peter Rabbit.** 💬 ❓

1 *How many sisters does Peter Rabbit have?*

He has three sisters.

2 Does Peter eat berries or radishes in the farmer's garden?

3 Do Peter's sisters go in the farmer's garden or their mother's garden?

4 What does Peter's mother say to Peter?

5 How does Peter feel at the end of the story, do you think?

14 **Circle the correct answers.**

1 Who has a happy day?

    a Peter has a happy day.

    b Peter's sisters have a happy day.

2 Who wants radishes from the farmer's garden?

    a Peter's mother wants radishes from the farmer's garden.

    b Peter wants radishes from the farmer's garden.

3 Who runs after Peter?

    a Peter's mother runs after Peter.

    b The farmer runs after Peter.

15 **Look, match, and write the words.** 📖 ✏️

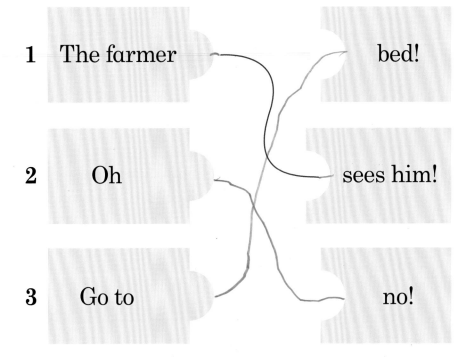

1 The farmer   bed!

2 Oh   sees him!

3 Go to   no!

1   The farmer sees him!

2   Oh no!

3   Go to bed!

16 **Order the story. Write 1—5.**

.... Peter eats lots of radishes.

___1___ Peter goes in the farmer's garden.

.... Peter runs home.

.... The farmer runs after Peter.

.... Peter runs in the shed.

17 **Look at the picture and read the questions. Write the answers.** 📖 ✏️ ❀

Peter Rabbit runs from the farmer's garden.

Peter runs and runs!

22

---

garden   home   farmer

---

1 Where is Peter?

He is in the farmer's ___garden___ .

2 Who is running after Peter?

The _____ is running after Peter.

3 Where does Peter want to go?

Peter wants to go _____ .

18 **Write the questions.** 📖 ✏️

1 (is) (Where) (Peter) (?)

Where is Peter?

2 (eat) (Peter) (What) (does) (?)

....

3 (Who) (Peter) (sees) (?)

....

4 (Peter) (runs) (after) (Who) (?)

....

5 (cannot) (Peter) (Who) (catch) (?)

....

19 Find the words.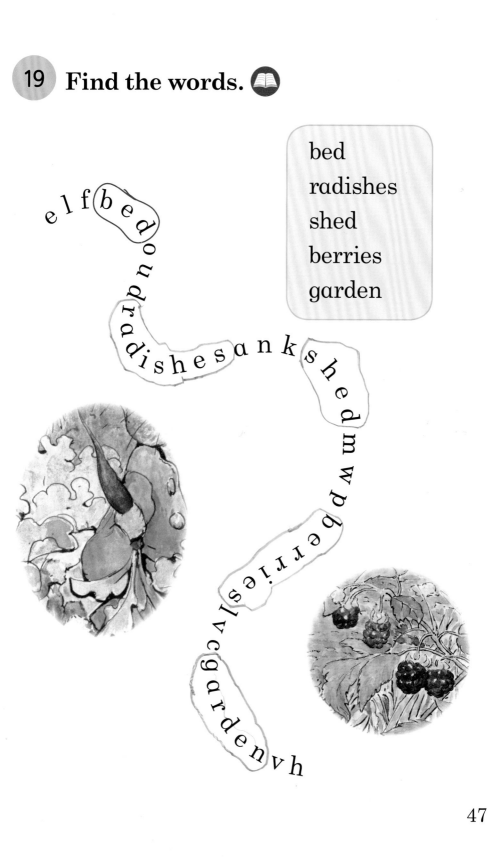

bed
radishes
shed
berries
garden

e l f b e d o u p d r a d i s h e s a n k s h e d m w p b e r r i e s l v c g a r d e n v h

Level 1

Ladybird Readers — Level 1 — Anansi Helps a Friend
978-0-241-25409-7

Ladybird Readers — Level 1 — Cinderella
978-0-241-25407-3

Ladybird Readers — Level 1 — The Enormous Turnip
978-0-241-25408-0

Ladybird Readers — Level 1 — On the Farm
978-0-241-25413-4

Ladybird Readers — Level 1 — Cars
978-0-241-28354-7

Ladybird Readers — Level 1 — Jon's Football Team
978-0-241-25411-0

Ladybird Readers — Level 1 — The Magic Porridge Pot
978-0-241-25406-6

Ladybird Readers — Level 1 — In the Garden
978-0-241-26220-7

Ladybird Readers — Level 1 — Fun with Old Things
978-0-241-26219-1

Ladybird Readers — Level 1 — Fairy Friends
978-0-241-28351-6

Ladybird Readers — Level 1 — Peter Rabbit Goes to the Island
978-0-241-25415-8

Ladybird Readers — Level 1 — Topsy and Tim Go to the Zoo
978-0-241-25414-1

Ladybird Readers — Level 1 — Topsy and Tim Go to the Farm
978-0-241-28355-4

Ladybird Readers — Level 1 — The Fair
978-0-241-28357-8

Ladybird Readers — Level 1 — Daddy Pig's Old Chair
978-0-241-28356-1

Ladybird Readers — Level 1 — Rex the Big Dinosaur
978-0-241-29741-4

Ladybird Readers — Level 1 — Peter Rabbit and the Radish Robber
978-0-241-29742-1

Ladybird Readers — Level 1 — Topsy and Tim Go to London
978-0-241-29743-8

Ladybird Readers — Level 1 — On a Boat
978-0-241-29744-5

Ladybird Readers — Level 1 — Baby Animals
978-0-241-29745-2

Ladybird Readers — Level 1 — The Tale of Peter Rabbit
978-0-241-31614-6

Ladybird Readers — Level 1 — Going Swimming
978-0-241-31613-9

Ladybird Readers — Level 1 — Decepticons in the Scrapyard
978-0-241-31943-7

Ladybird Readers — Level 1 — Deserts
978-0-241-31608-5

Now you're ready for Level 2!